Ssh!
Don't Wake the Baby

10 Publishing
a division of **10** of those.com

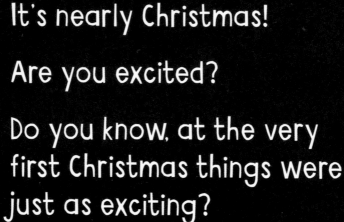

It's nearly Christmas!

Are you excited?

Do you know, at the very first Christmas things were just as exciting?

There
were
angels.

There were
shepherds.

baaa baaa

And there was a baby.
A baby who would
change things forever!

Have you got a baby in your house?

A baby is very small. But it can make a very big noise!

Everyone is so pleased when, at last, the baby goes to sleep.

We tiptoe round and say:

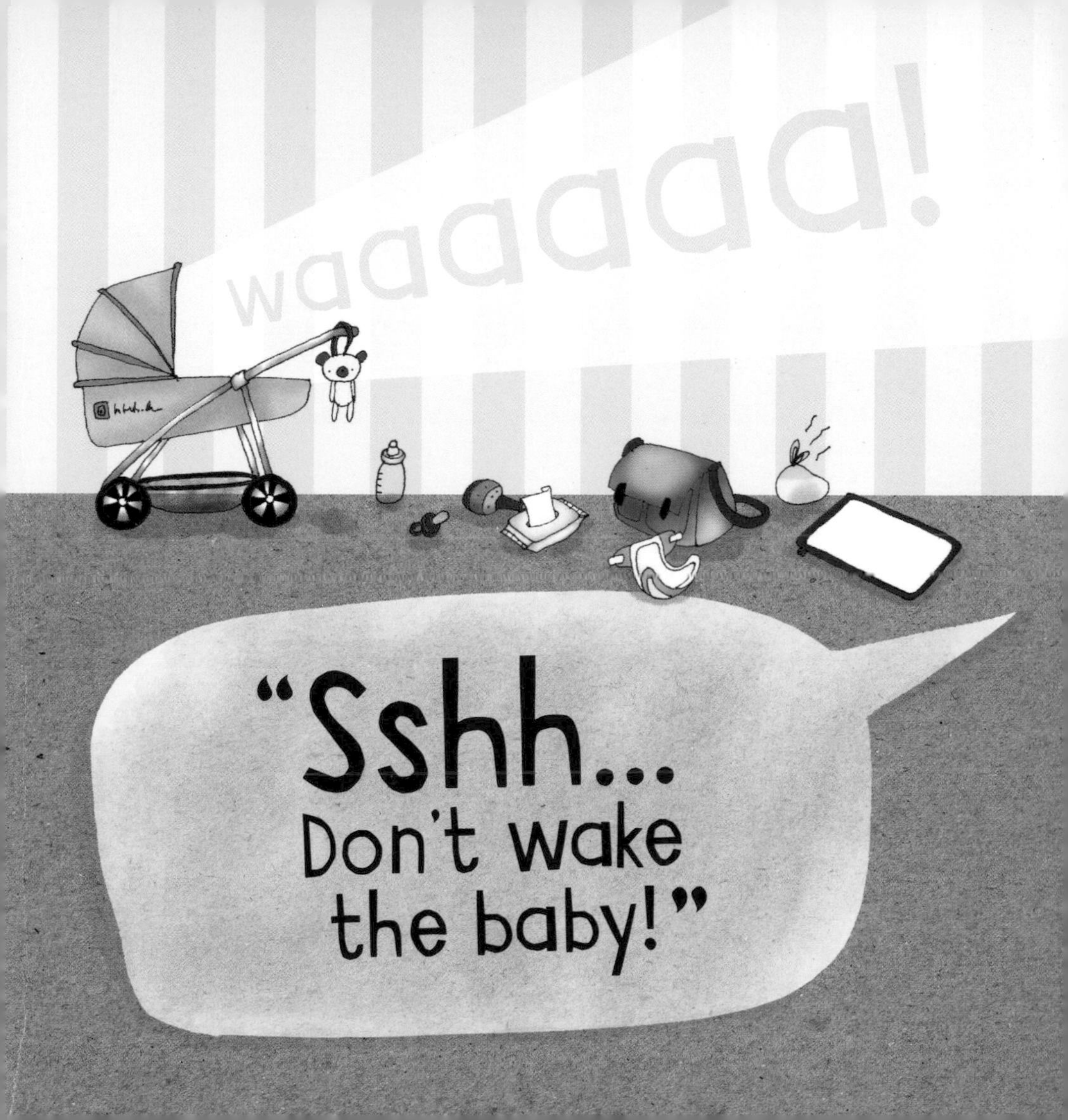
waaaaaa!
"Sshh... Don't wake the baby!"

Whatever happens...
don't **wake** the baby!

Creep past her room.

Don't knock his pram.

"Sshh...
Don't wake the baby!"

2000 years ago in Bethlehem a baby was born. He looked like every other baby.

His name was Jesus.

Baby Jesus.

He cried when
he was **hungry**.

He cried when
he was **tired**.

And he made a
great big **noise**.
Just like every other baby!

Mary must have been
so pleased when, at
last, he closed his eyes.

Joseph must have been
so glad when, at last,
he went to sleep.

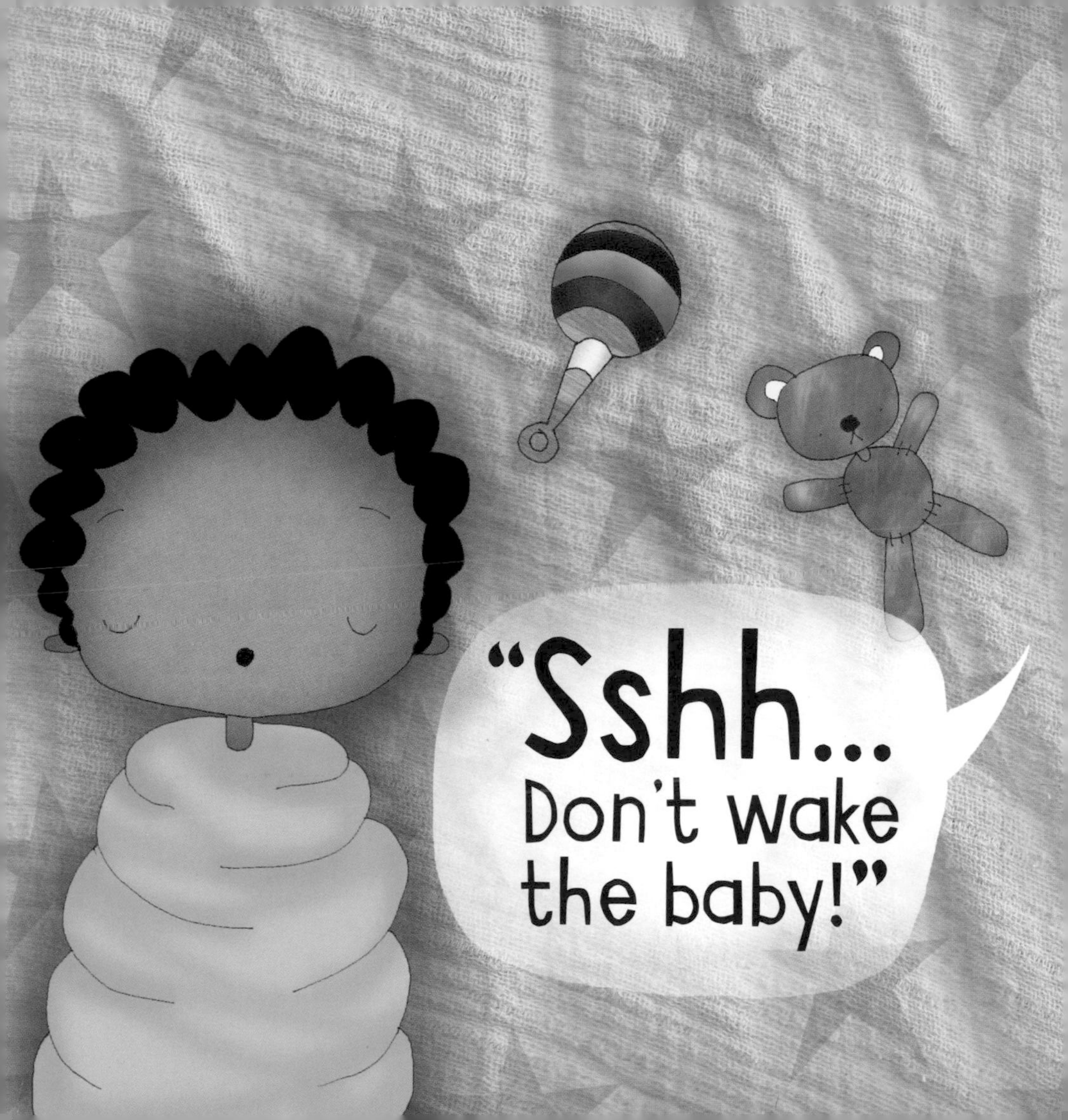
"Sshh...
Don't wake
the baby!"

Maybe Joseph
tiptoed round
the stable.

Maybe Mary told
the shepherds:

No
running.

No
singing.

No
shouting.

Creep past the manger.

Baby Jesus looked like every other baby... except... The Bible says this......► Jesus gave up his place with God and made himself nothing. Jesus left beautiful Heaven.

Jesus is the Son of God!

Jesus who made everything, made himself nothing.

He made himself tiny. He was born as a baby.

He made himself tiny. He was born as a baby.

Jesus stepped down to this earth.

He became a baby.

Why did he do that?

Jesus was born as a baby
so that Jesus the man
could die on the cross.

Because he loves people.
You and me.

And because he wants
people (you and me) to
be part of God's family.

We can be **friends**
with God!

There are lots of lovely things about Christmas.

There are lots of exciting things about Christmas.

But the loveliest thing of all is that Jesus was born.

The most exciting thing of all is that Jesus gave up his place with God and made himself nothing.

You might be having all sorts of visitors this Christmas.

Look out for a baby.

Look out for everyone waiting for the baby to close her eyes and go to sleep. Look out for everyone whispering:

"Sshh...
Don't wake the baby!"

Remember Jesus.

Jesus is the Son of God!

He stepped down from Heaven and became a baby. For us.

Find this story in the Bible in Philippians chapter 2 and Luke chapter 2.